AME GOES TO SCHOOL IN JAPAN

A Cool Cat's School Life in Japan

Story by Mami Bacera and Mark Bacera
Illustrated by Mami Bacera

Copyright ® 2023 Rounded Specs Publishing LLC
ISBN 978-1-952343-10-0

I'm visiting from America.
Today is my first day of school in Japan.

If you go to elementary school in Japan,
having this bag, called a **Randoseru**, is a must.
Looks like I have a hand-me-down from Mae.

Let's take a look at what's inside my **Randoseru**.
There are a bunch of unfamiliar items inside.

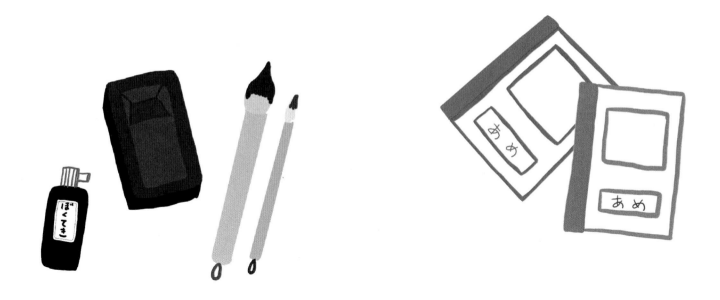

I don't know exactly how to use them yet,
but I'll figure them out.

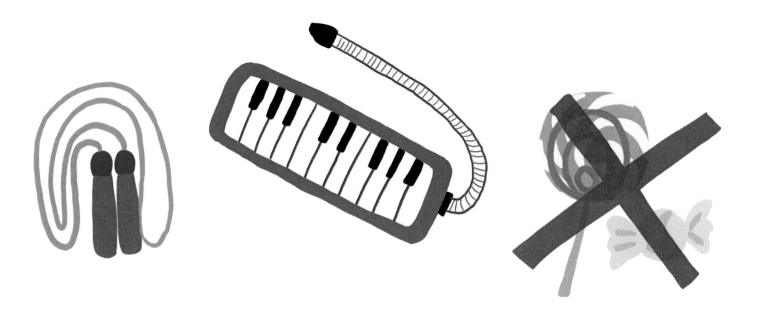

WAIT...WHERE ARE THE SNACKS?!?!

Do you know how elementary schoolers
in Japan get to school?

First, we meet up
in the morning at a meeting place
called a **Shuugoubasho**.

The oldest kid in the group is
our group leader, or **Hanchou**.

He takes the lead and we all walk in
a single line all the way to school.

I'M SO TIRED!!!!

We *finally* made it to school.

The school year in Japan starts
in the beginning of April.

At this time, you can see many
beautiful, pink flowers in the trees.

These are **Sakura,** or cherry blossoms,
and they're very pretty.

By the way, can you find
me in this picture?

CAN YOU ALSO SPOT THESE KIDS?

- ☐ a boy running to school
- ☐ a boy falling down
- ☐ a girl whose hat is blowing away
- ☐ a girl in a striped shirt

Before we can come inside, we have to
change into our indoor shoes,
or **Uwabaki**, to keep the building clean.

Oops, I don't even own a pair of shoes.
I better wipe my feet before going inside!

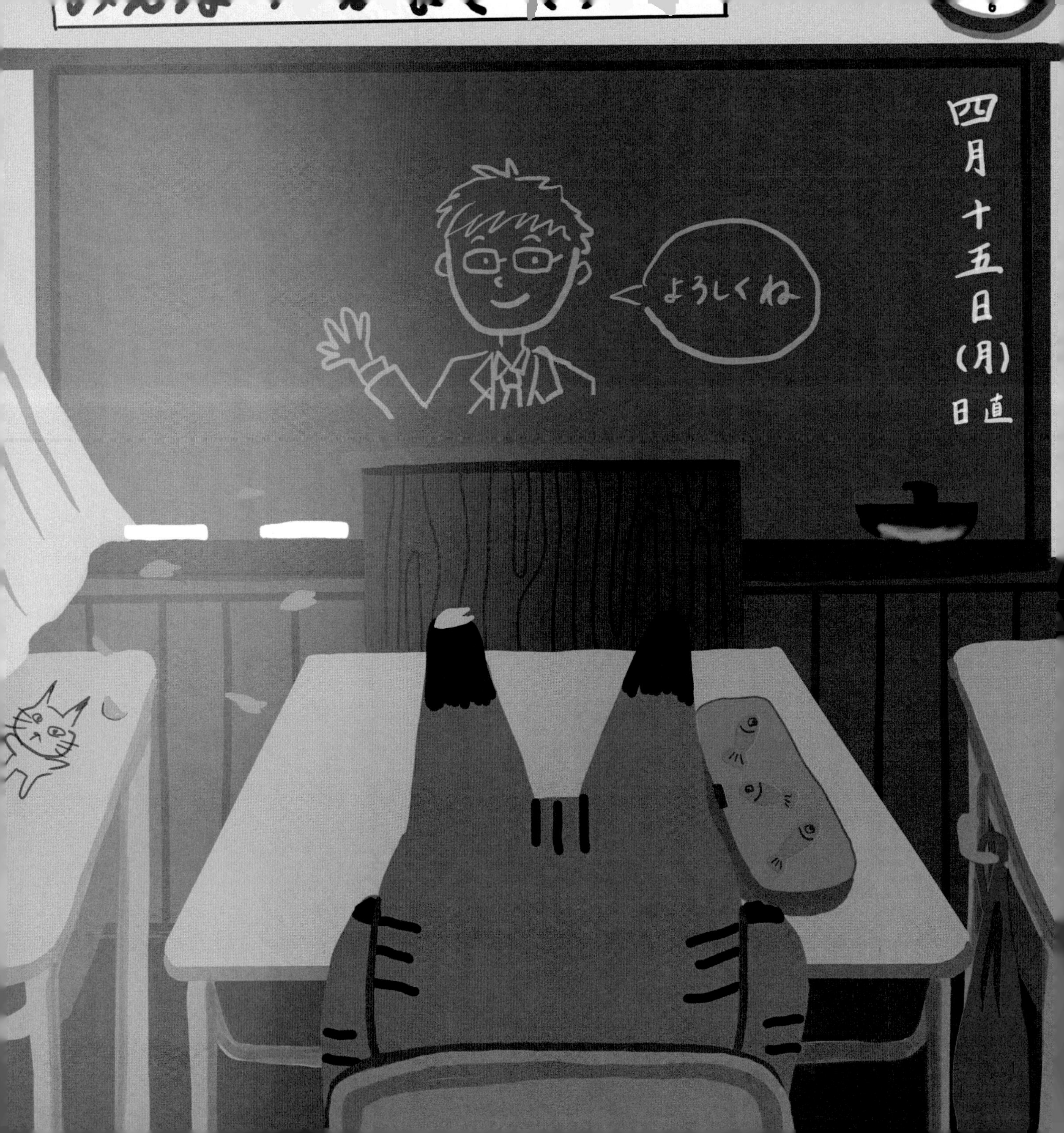
よろしくね
四月十五日(月)
日直

Phew, I finally made it to my classroom.

I'm very excited to learn new
things and make new friends.

The teacher, or **Sensei**, isn't here yet,
but he *looks* like a nice human.

My very first class is Japanese Calligraphy, or **Shuuji**.

The teacher told us to write any **Kanji***,
that we knew—so I wrote my name!

雨, or **Ame** (pronounced like *Ah-meh*),
means *rain* in Japanese.

*Note: **Kanji** originated from China and
is one of the three writing systems used in Japan.

GYM CLASS.

Have you seen these *sports* before?

The first thing I tried was called the **Tobi Bako**, or literally, a jumping box.

Kids jump over each level until they can't clear it. To no one's surprise, I'm *very* good.

After that we moved on to jump roping, but—

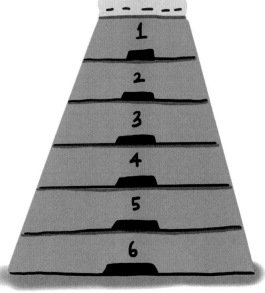

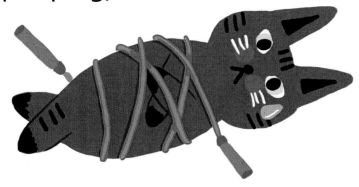

THIS ISN'T THE JUMP–ROPING I KNOW FROM BACK HOME!!!

MUSIC CLASS.

I've never seen anything like this either.
It's called a pianica...I guess it's a
cross between a piano and a
harmonica.

Humans make the strangest things sometimes...

I'M STARVING!!!

It's *finally* lunch time.
They call it **Kyuushoku** here in Japan.

Instead of teachers serving food to students,
students serve food to each other.

Japanese schools do this to teach kids
responsibility, hard work, and service.

Doing this is actually pretty fun, but—

I CAN'T STOP DROOLING!!!

Today's menu is...

I heard that the menu changes every day.
They usually include bread or rice, soup, salad,
meat, dessert, and a box of milk—my favorite!!!

I'M FULL... (BURP)

That lunch was *really* great!

Next up is another new experience—
school cleaning time!

Kids from all grade levels are put into separate
cleaning groups and are assigned to different
rooms and areas throughout the school.

Some kids sweep, some kids mop,
and some kids even clean toilets!

Today, my group is in charge of mopping the hallway.

LOOK AT ME—I'M A CLEANING MACHINE!!!

Ding dong! Ding dong!

CLASSES ARE FINALLY OVER!!!

Phew. That was an exciting first day of school.

I learned a lot and even made some new friends.

We get to walk home with different people
than we go to school with in the morning.
Yay! So many new friends.

Today has been *so* fun! I can't wait to see
what new things I will learn tomorrow.
I hope you got to enjoy the experience as well!

Oh darn, I've got to go.
Homework is calling.
Bye for now!

THE END

CAN YOU FIND ALL THESE HIDDEN THINGS?

Japanese sweet orange
(mikan)

Love note

Bucket

Blackboard eraser
(kokuban-keshi)

Wall clock
(tokei)

Black cat

LET'S LEARN JAPANESE!

Randoseru （ランドセル） Japanese school bag

Shuugoubasho （しゅうごうばしょ） meeting place

Hanchou （はんちょう） group leader

Sakura （さくら） cherry blossom

Uwabaki （うわばき） indoor shoes

Sensei （せんせい） teacher

Shuuji （しゅうじ） Japanese calligraphy

Ame （あめ） rain

Tobi Bako （とびばこ） vaulting box/horse

Kyuushoku （きゅうしょく） school lunch

Ame Goes to School in Japan

A Cool Cat's School Life in Japan

Story by Mami Bacera and Mark Bacera
Illustrated by Mami Bacera

ISBN 978-1-952343-10-0

Website:

www.roundedspecspublishing.com

Facebook:

FB.me/roundedspecspublishing

Instagram:
@roundedspecspublishing

About the Author

Mami Bacera is a bilingual English teacher and mother who has always had a passion for illustrating and stories.

She believes that the most important thing in life is family, and strives to find the simple things that bring true happiness.

Mami insists that every person has talents within and urges others to search them out and cultivate them.

This book is inspired by her real-life, nonchalant, yet easy-going cat named Ame.

Email:
info@roundedspecspublishing.com

Authors love reviews! To leave one, visit:
www.amazon.com/dp/B0CHXQT931

Other Books and Creations By Mami Bacera

- Ame Goes to Japan
- A Day with Mae
- Who is Ame?
- Ame Goes to Shimane
- Ame Goes to Okinawa
- Ame Goes to Hiroshima

Other Rounded Specs Books

- The Poo Poo Book
- The Belly Button Book
- The Fart Book
- The Booger Book
- The Snot Book
- The Tooth Book
- The Ear Wax Book
- The Stinky Feet Book
- The Sweat Book
- The Tear Book
- The Spit Book
- Baby Poop
- I Shaved Half of Daddy's Face
- Isdaman
- A Naughty Kid's Christmas ABC
- I'm an Alien-Vampire and I'm Proud of it

Please note that some of the above titles have yet to be published. To support us and be notified when new books are in the works and released, send us an email at info@roundedspecspublishing.com

Made in the USA
Las Vegas, NV
15 May 2024

89957564R00019

the verve
URBAN HYMNS

Bitter Sweet Symphony	2
Sonnet	6
The Rolling People	14
The Drugs Don't Work	24
Catching The Butterfly	30
Neon Wilderness	36
Space And Time	38
Weeping Willow	46
Lucky Man	58
One Day	64
This Time	68
Velvet Morning	53
Come On	72

International MUSIC Publications

International Music Publications Limited
Griffin House 161 Hammersmith Road London W6 8BS England

Folio © 2001 International Music Publications Ltd
Griffin House, 161 Hammersmith Road, London W6 8BS, England

Bitter Sweet Symphony

Words and Music by
Richard Ashcroft, Mick Jagger
and Keith Richards

Sonnet

Words and Music by
Richard Ashcroft

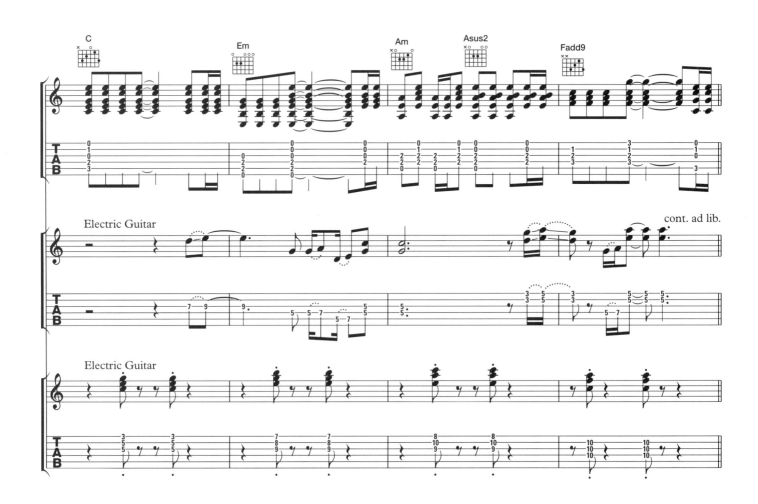

8

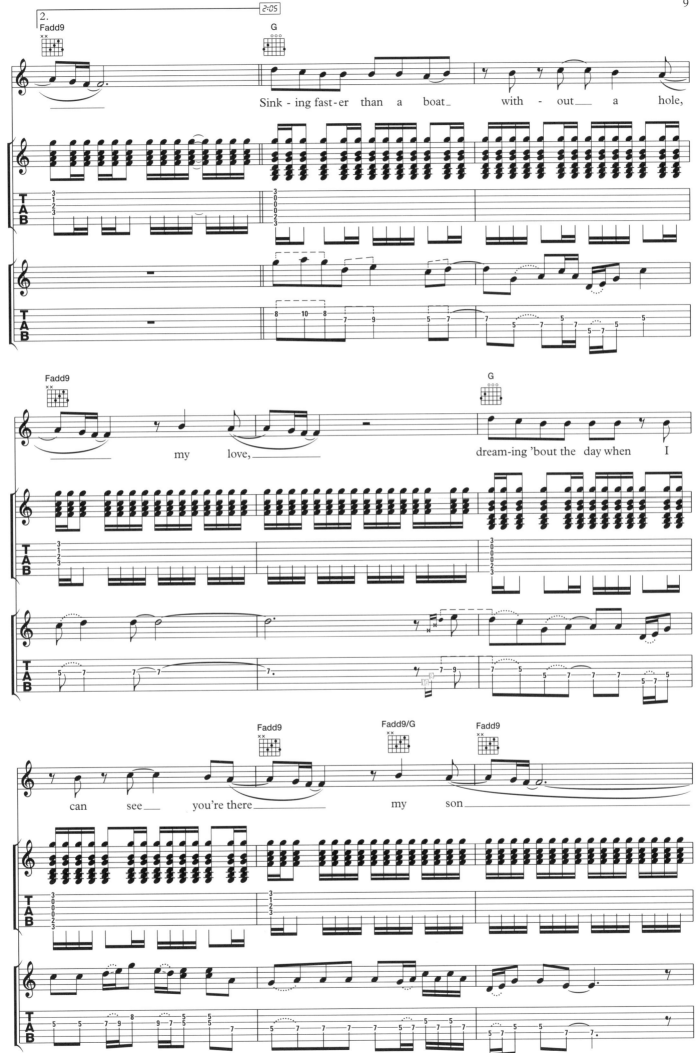

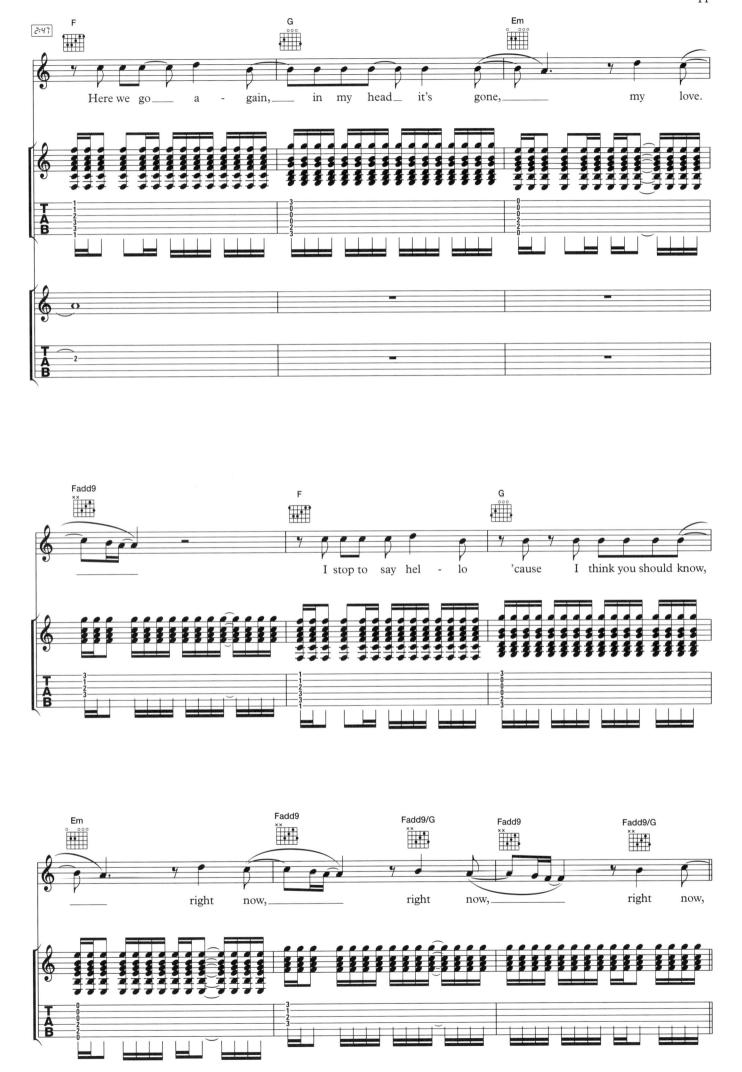

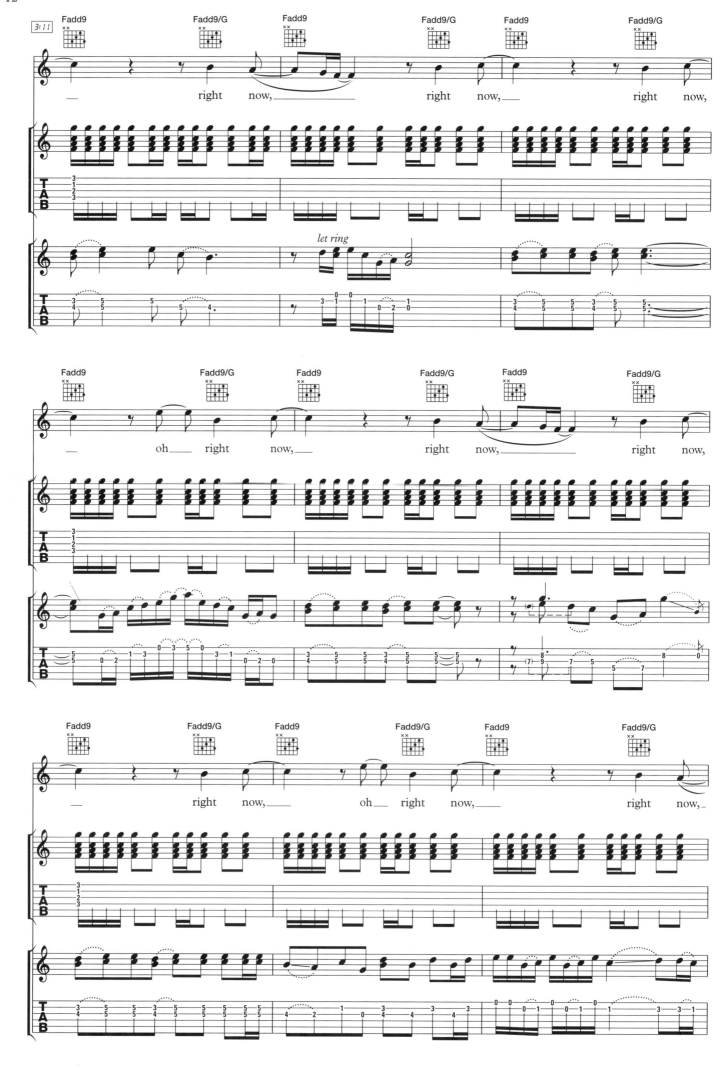

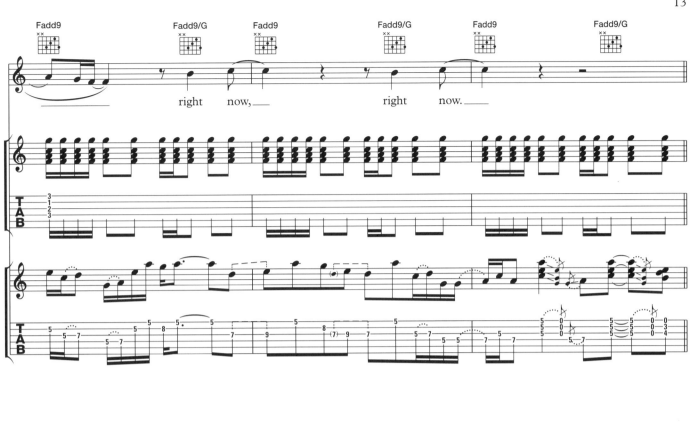

right now,___ right now.___

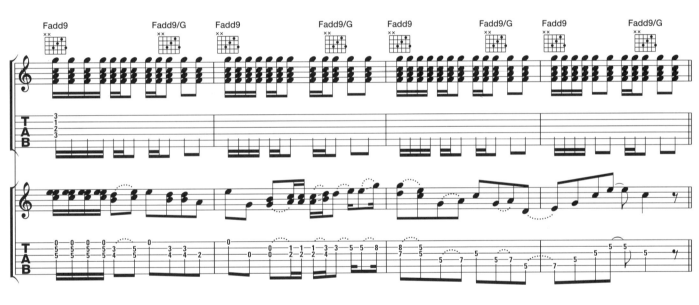

repeat to fade

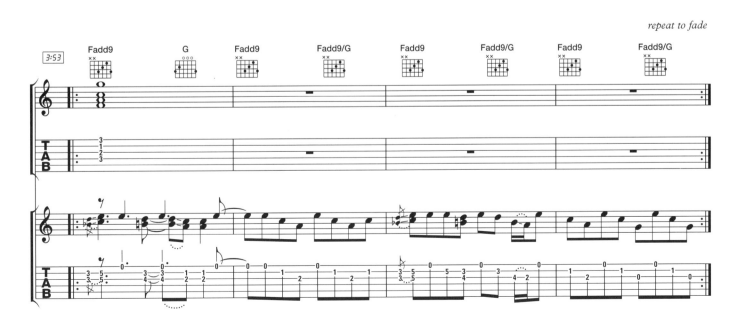

The Rolling People

Words and Music by
Simon Jones, Peter Salisbury,
Nick McCabe and Richard Ashcroft

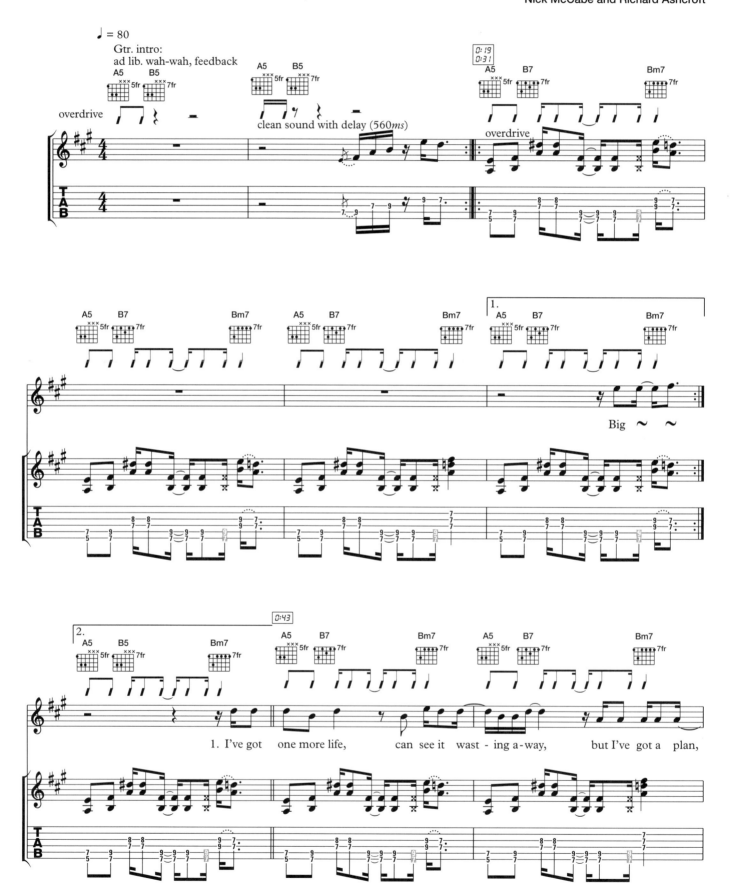

1. I've got one more life, can see it wast-ing a-way, but I've got a plan,

ah, _____ coz death has no fans. _____ And
yeah, _____ to my rot - ten soul. _____ And

(%) here we are___ the roll — ing peo — ple, can't stay for long, we got to go. ___
here we are___ the roll — ing peo — ple, don't ask why, _ we don't know.

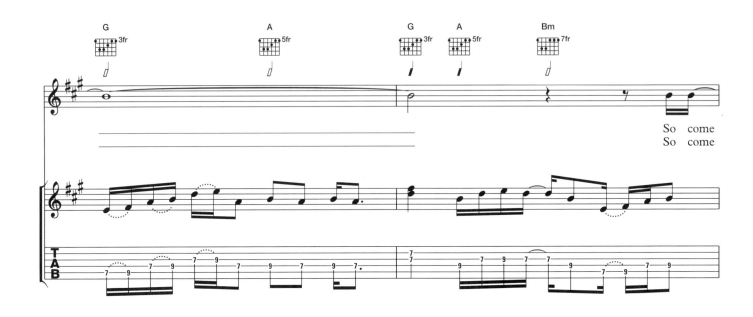

So come
So come

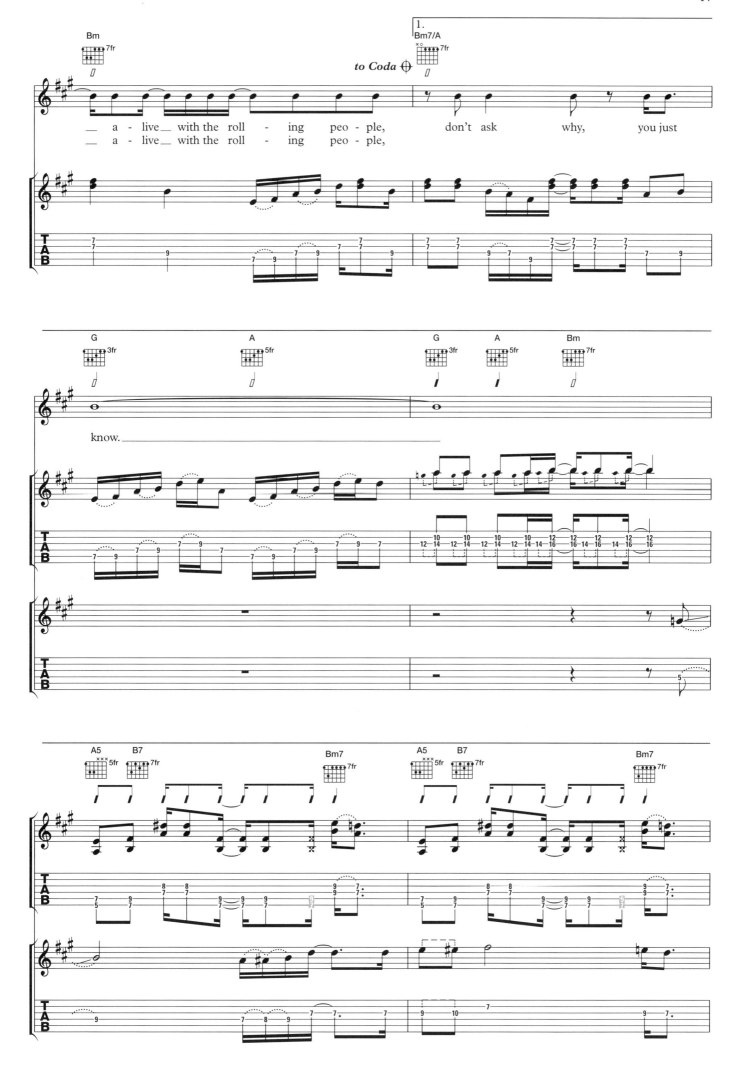

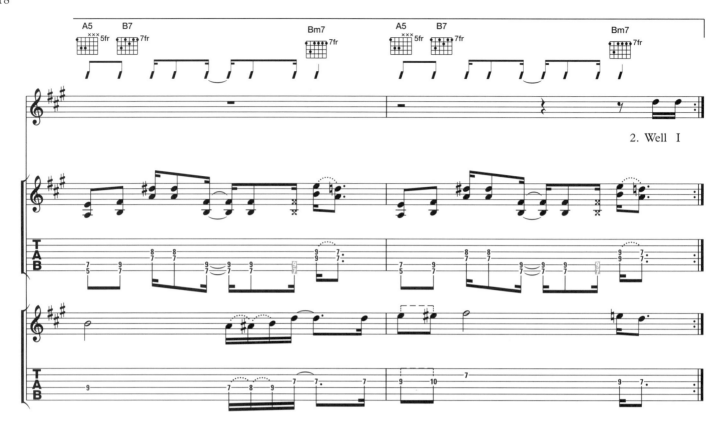

2. Well I

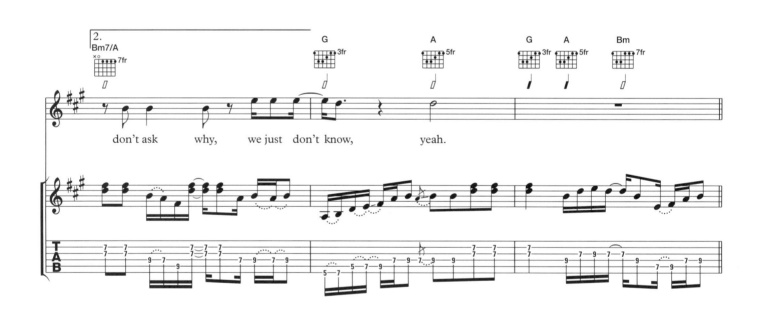

don't ask   why,   we just   don't know,   yeah.

clean sound

2:53

Seems that I know which way _ I'm go - ing to, _____ the

clean sound

sim.

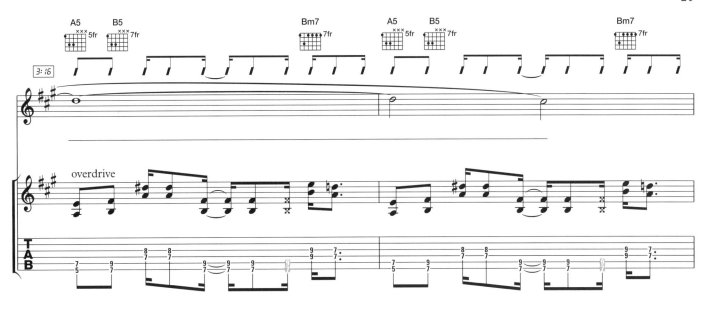

don't ask why, we don't know___ now, yeah.___

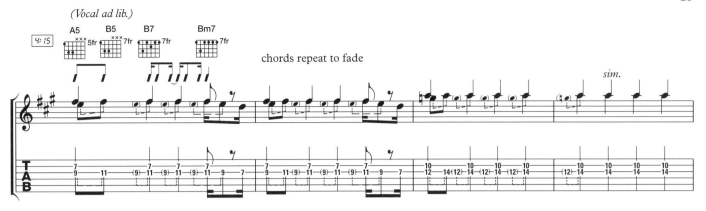

The Drugs Don't Work

Words and Music by
Richard Ashcroft

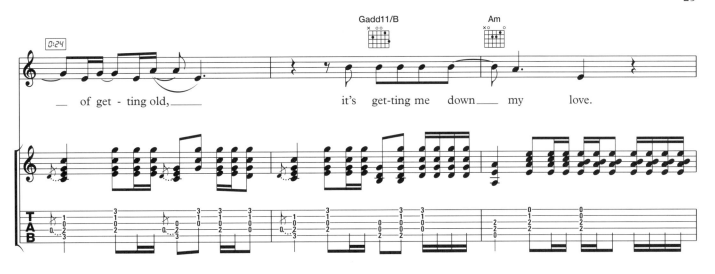

of get - ting old,___ it's get-ting me down___ my love.

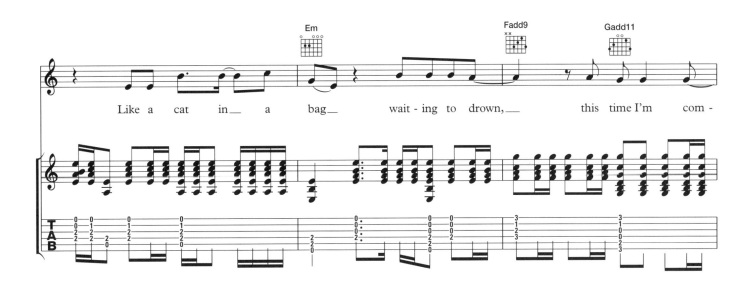

Like a cat in___ a bag___ wait - ing to drown,___ this time I'm com -

- ing down. (1.) And I hope___

Electric Guitar

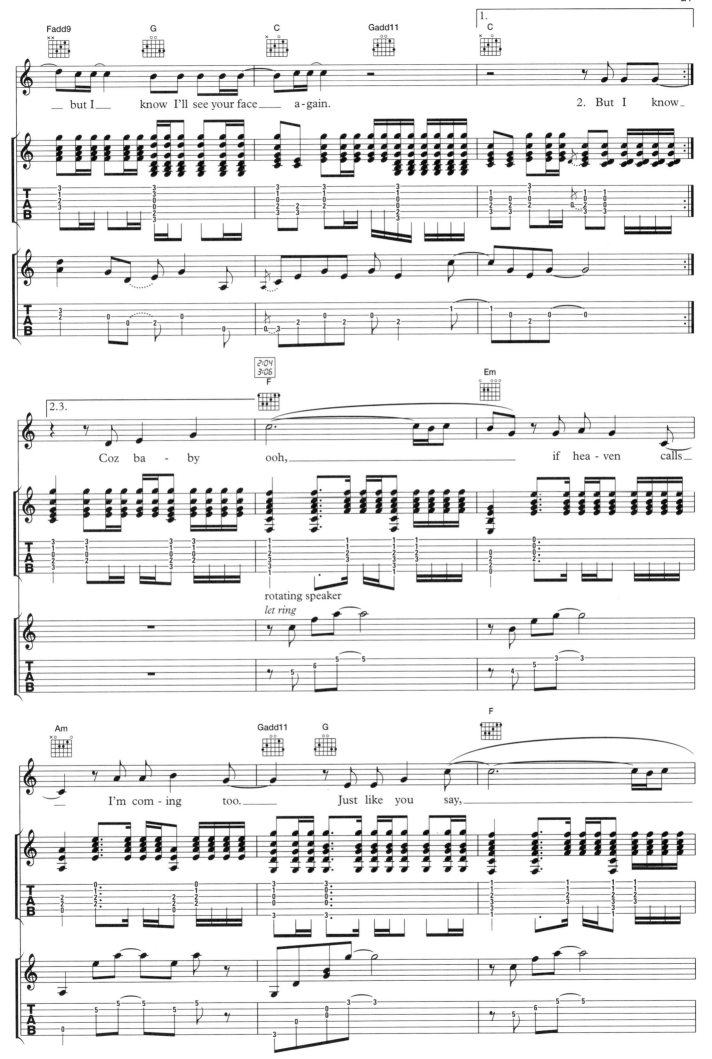

Catching The Butterfly

Words and Music by
Simon Jones, Peter Salisbury,
Nick McCabe, Simon Tong
and Richard Ashcroft

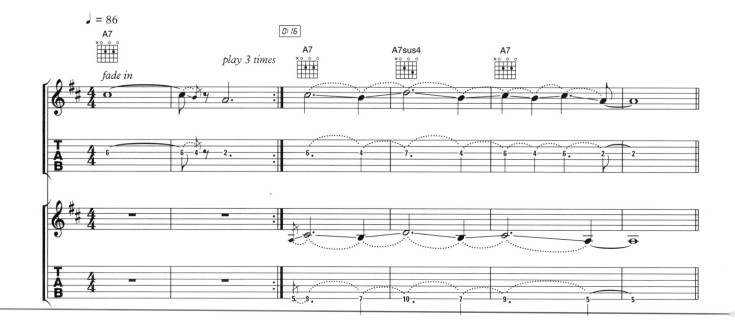

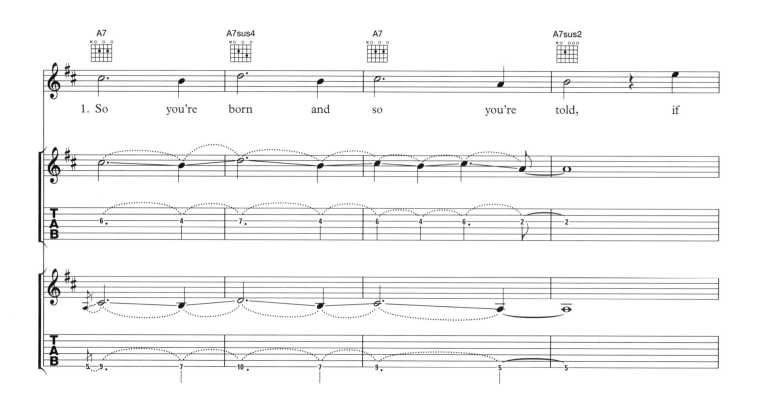

Neon Wilderness

Words and Music by
Simon Jones, Peter Salisbury,
Nick McCabe and Richard Ashcroft

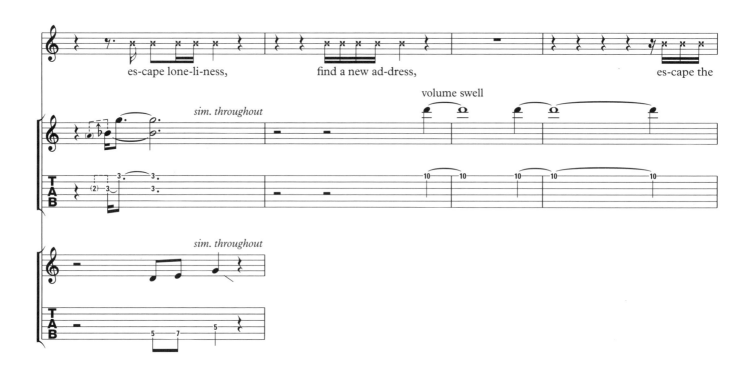

Space And Time

Words and Music by
Richard Ashcroft

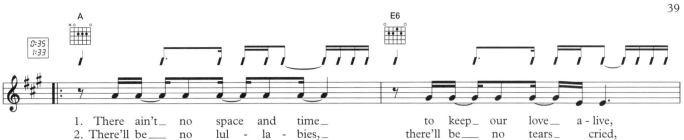

1. There ain't__ no space and time__ to keep__ our love__ a - live,
2. There'll be__ no lul - la - bies,__ there'll be__ no tears__ cried,

we have ex - is - tence and that's all we share.___ There ain't no real__ truth,
we feel known 'cause we don't see_____ that if__ we real - ly cared

there ain't no real__ light, keep on push - ing cause I know it's there.___
and__ we real - ly loved, think of all the joy we'd feel._____

we have ex - is - tence and that's all we share, we have ex - is - tence and that's

Acoustic Guitar

ad lib. to end

all we share, we have ex - is - tence and that's all we share.

fade out

Weeping Willow

Words and Music by
Richard Ashcroft

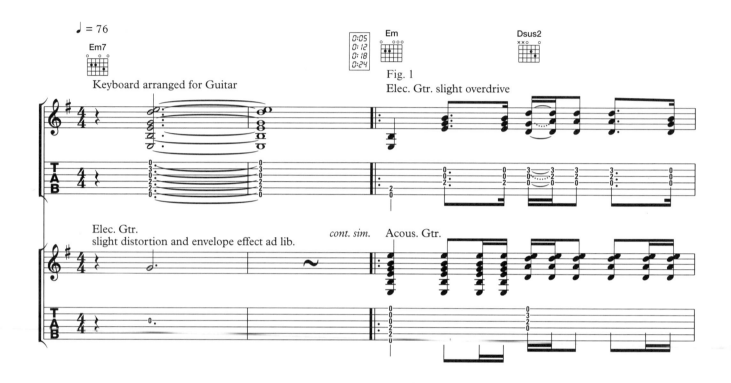

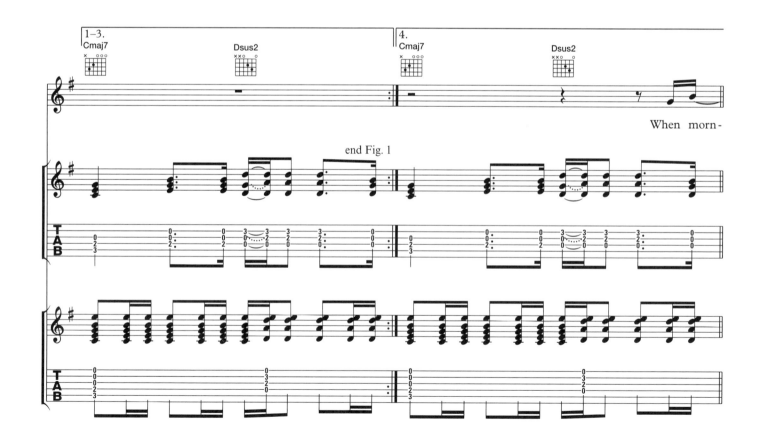

When morn-

48

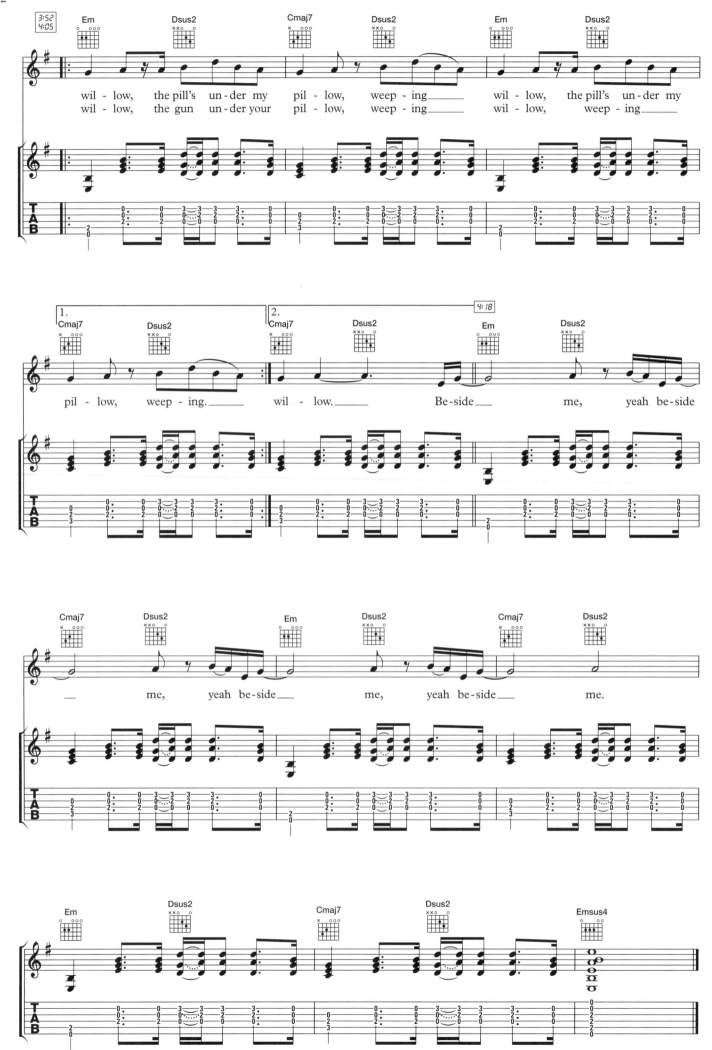

Velvet Morning

Words and Music by
Richard Ashcroft

try-ing to tell you a-bout__ my life__ and my__ tongue is twist-ed, I'm__ more

Electric Guitar

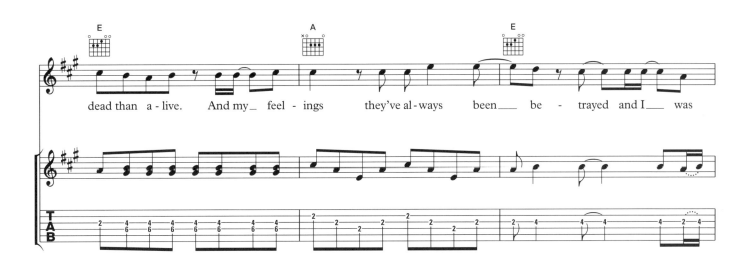

dead than a-live. And my__ feel-ings they've al-ways been__ be-trayed and I__ was

born__ a lit-tle da-maged man, look what they've made. I said don't__ you

Acoustic Guitar

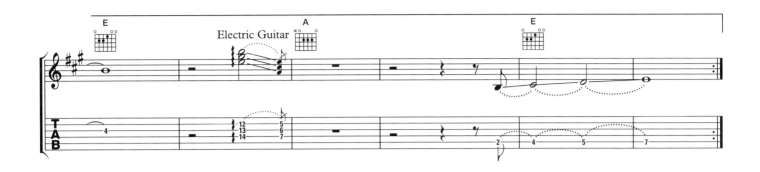

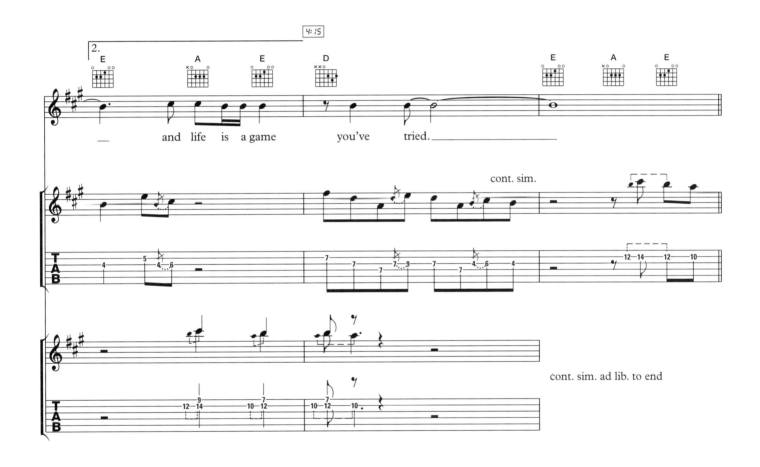

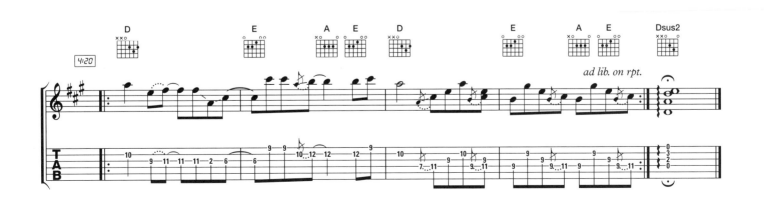

Lucky Man

Words and Music by
Richard Ashcroft

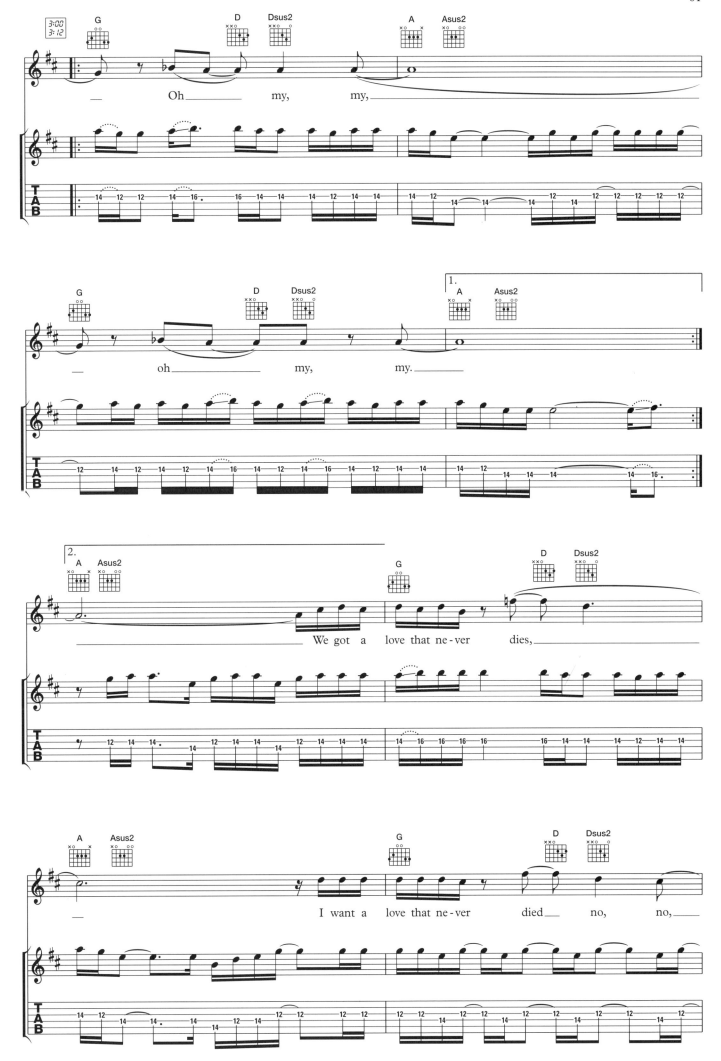

One Day

Words and Music by
Richard Ashcroft

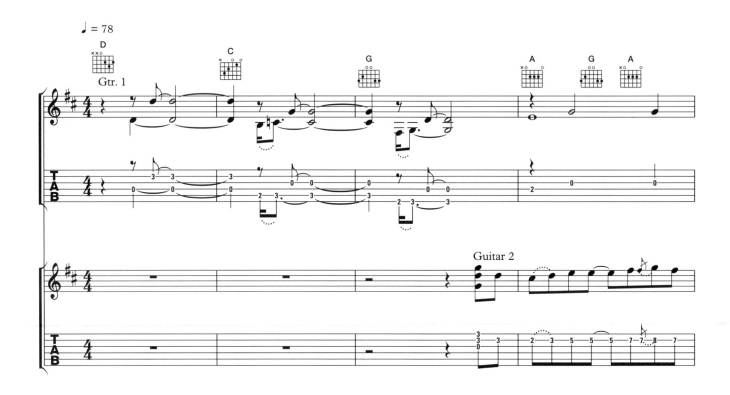

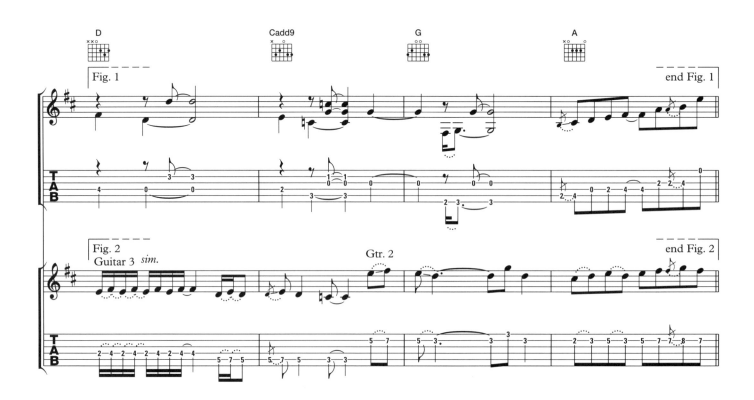

with Fig. 1 ad lib.
with Fig. 2 ad lib.

0:24

D   Cadd9   G   A

1. One day may-be we will dance a-gain un-der fi — ery sky,

D   Cadd9   G   A

one day may-be we will love a-gain, love that ne — ver dies.

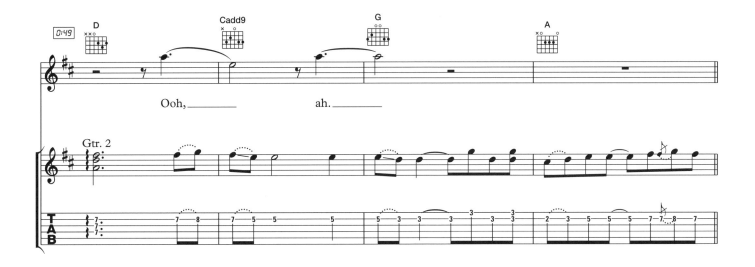

0:49

D   Cadd9   G   A

Ooh, _____ ah. _____

Gtr. 2

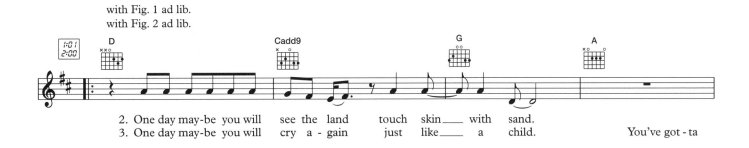

with Fig. 1 ad lib.
with Fig. 2 ad lib.

1:01
2:00

D   Cadd9   G   A

2. One day may-be you will see the land touch skin__ with sand.
3. One day may-be you will cry a-gain just like__ a child.   You've got-ta

D   Cadd9   G   A

You've been swim-ming in the lone - ly sea__ with no com - pa - ny.__
tie your-self to the mast my friend__ and the storm__ will end.__

Oh_____ don't__ you wan-na find, can't__ you hear there's beau-ty in life.___ The times

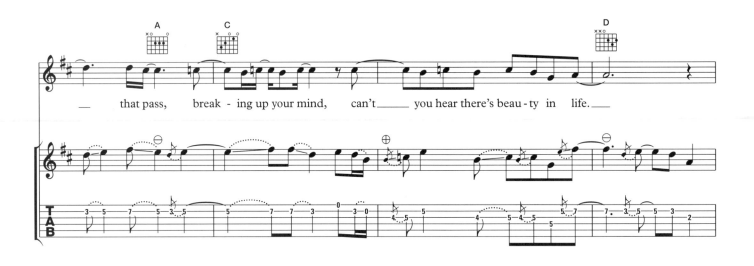

__ that pass, break - ing up your mind, can't_____ you hear there's beau - ty in life.___

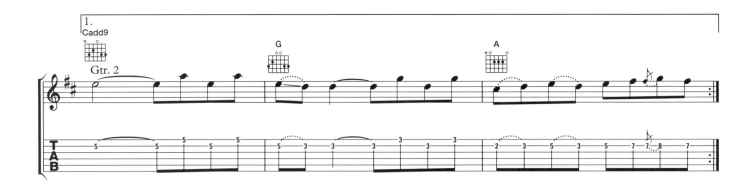

Oh_____ you're too___ a-fraid to touch, too___ a-fraid you'd like it too much._ The roads,

the times, break - ing up your mind, can't you hear there's beau-ty in life.

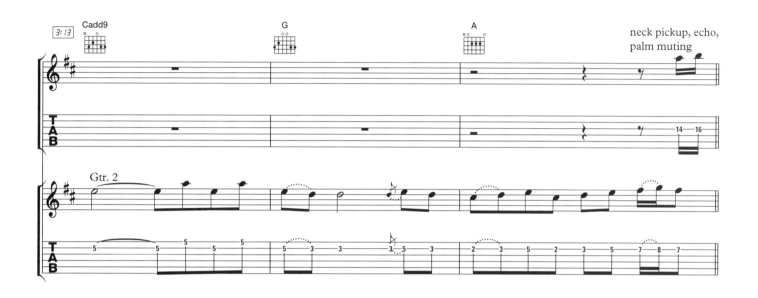

neck pickup, echo, palm muting

Gtr. 2

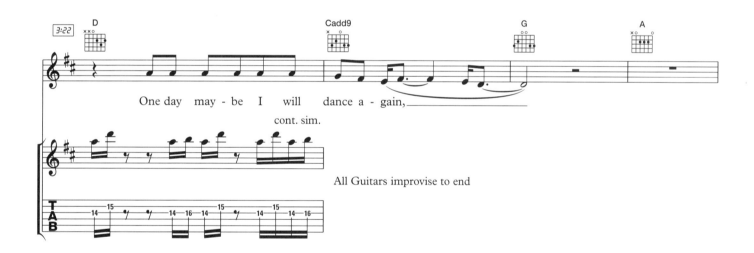

One day may - be I will dance a - gain,

cont. sim.

All Guitars improvise to end

one day may-be I will love a - gain.

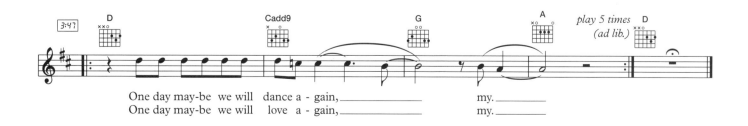

play 5 times (ad lib.)

One day may-be we will dance a - gain, my.
One day may-be we will love a - gain, my.

This Time

Words and Music by
Richard Ashcroft

♩ = 102

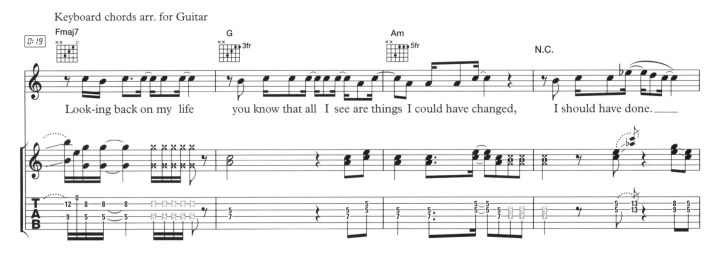

Look-ing back on my life you know that all I see are things I could have changed, I should have done.___

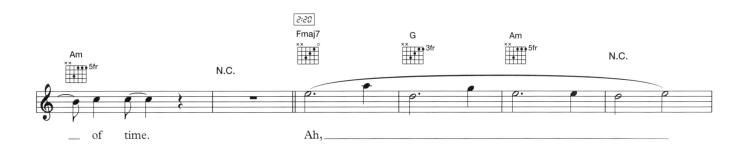

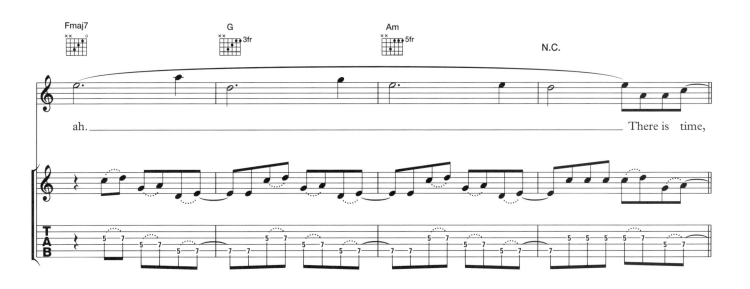

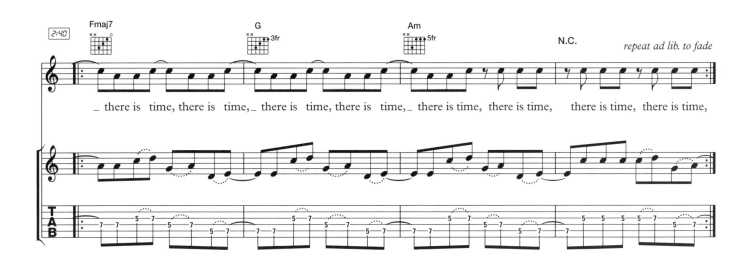

Come On

Words and Music by
Simon Jones, Peter Salisbury,
Nick McCabe and Richard Ashcroft

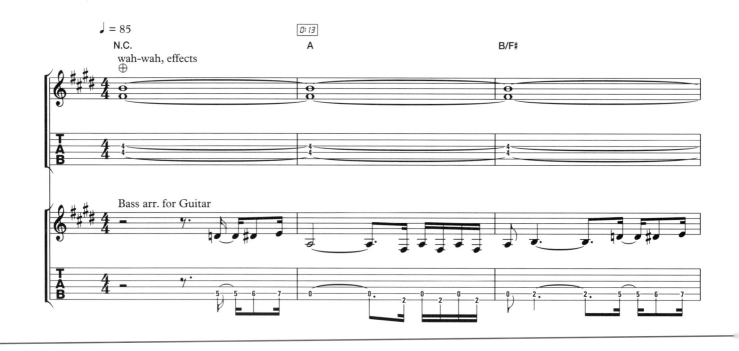

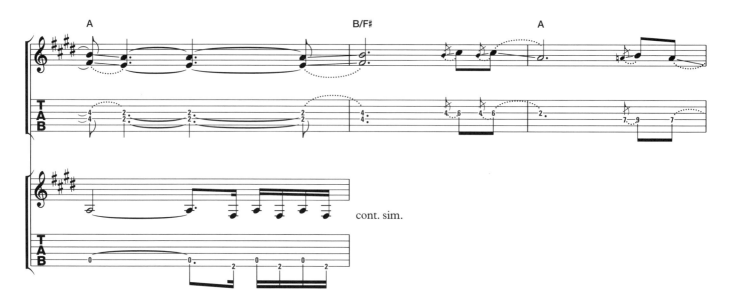

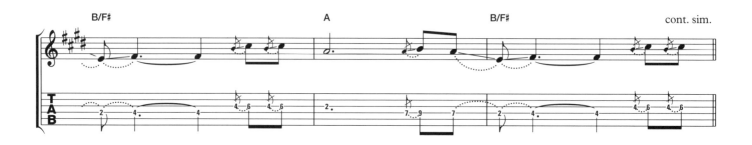

2. I must be go-ing in - sane,_____ I called the doc-tor so he can re-lieve my pain.

with wah-wah slide guitar ad lib.

_____ Well he's got a lit-tle pill_____ for me, just a lit-tle lux - u-ry,___ help me through my day,_____ yeah.

with Fig. 1

Come on, let the spi - rit in-side you, don't wait to be found, come a-long with our sound.____

Let this spi-rit move you, let the weight come off con-fuse you, I ne-ver meant no one to get nas - ty._____

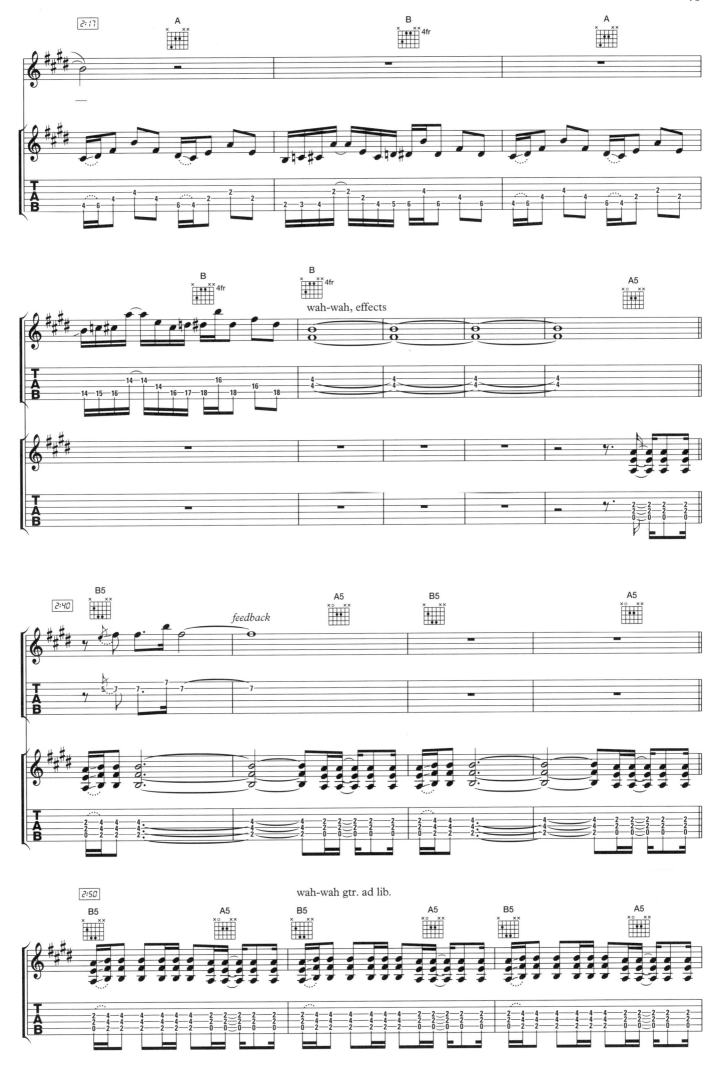

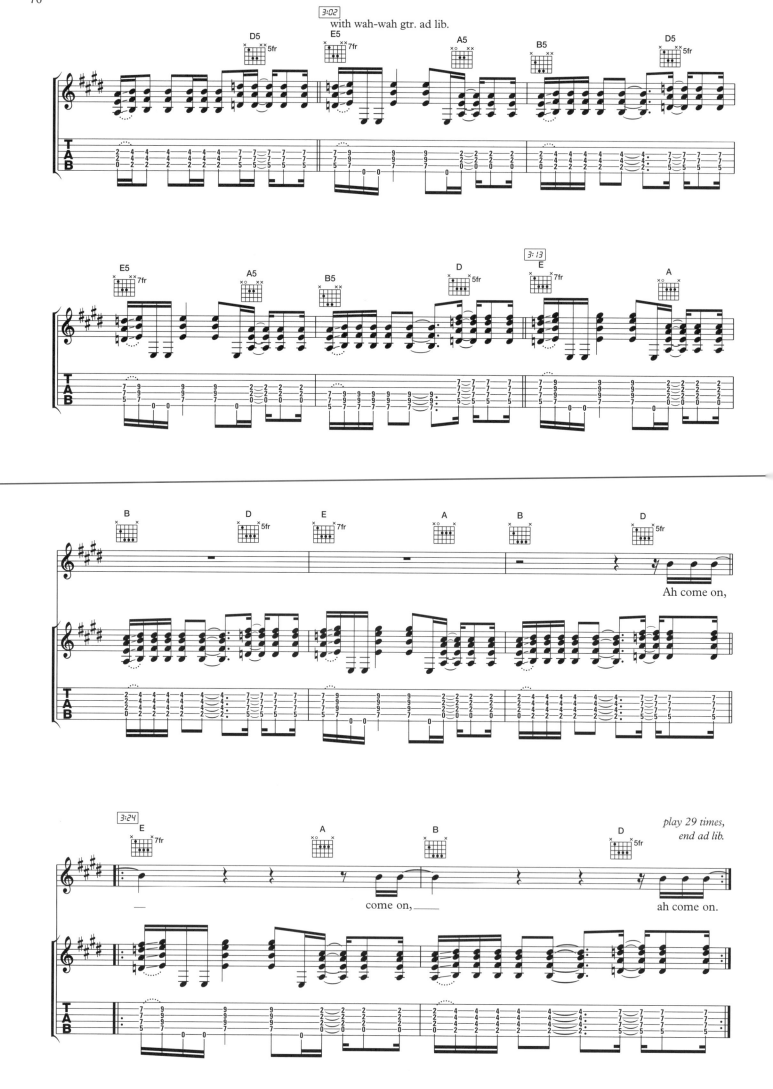

Notation and Tablature Explained

Open C chord

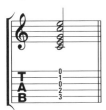

Scale of E major

High E (1st) string
B (2nd) string
G (3rd) string
D (4th) string
A (5th) string
Low E (6th) string

Bent Notes

The note fretted is always shown first. Variations in pitch achieved by string bending are enclosed within this symbol ⌐ ¬. If you aren't sure how far to bend the string, playing the notes indicated without bending gives a guide to the pitches to aim for. The following examples cover the most common string bending techniques:

Example 1
Play the D, bend up one tone (two half-steps) to E.

Example 4
Pre-bend: fret the D, bend up one tone to E, then pick.

Example 2
Play the D, bend up one tone to E then release bend to sound D. Only the first note is picked.

Example 5
Play the A and D together, then bend the B-string up one tone to sound B.

Example 3
Fast bend: Play the D, then bend up one tone to E as quickly as possible.

Example 6
Play the D and F♯ together, then bend the G-string up one tone to E, and the B-string up a semitone to G.

Additional guitaristic techniques have been notated as follows:

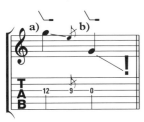

Tremolo Bar
Alter pitch using tremolo bar. Where possible, the pitch to aim for is shown.
a) Play the G; use the bar to drop the pitch to E.
b) Play the open G; use the bar to 'divebomb', i.e. drop the pitch as far as possible.

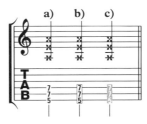

Mutes
a) Right hand mute
Mute strings by resting the right hand on the strings just above the bridge.
b) Left hand mute
Damp the strings by releasing left hand pressure just after the notes sound.
c) Unpitched mute
Damp the strings with the left hand to produce a percussive sound.

Hammer on and Pull off
Play first note, sound next note by 'hammering on', the next by 'pulling off'. Only the first note is picked.

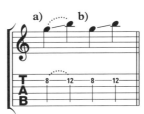

Glissando
a) Play first note, sound next note by sliding up string. Only the first note is picked.
b) As above, but pick second note.

Natural Harmonics
Touch the string over the fret marked, and pick to produce a bell-like tone. The small notes show the resultant pitch, where necessary.

a)   b)

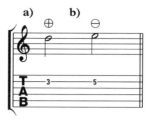

Slide Guitar
a) Play using slide.
b) Play without slide.

Artificial Harmonics
Fret the lowest note, touch string over fret indicated by diamond notehead and pick. Small notes show the resultant pitch.

Vibrato
Apply vibrato, by 'shaking' note or with tremolo bar. As vibrato is so much a matter of personal taste and technique, it is indicated only where essential.

Pinch Harmonics
Fret the note as usual, but 'pinch' or 'squeeze' the string with the picking hand to produce a harmonic overtone. Small notes show the resultant pitch.

Pick Scratch
Scrape the pick down the strings – this works best on the wound strings.

Microtones
A downwards arrow means the written pitch is lowered by less than a semitone; an upwards arrow raises the written pitch.

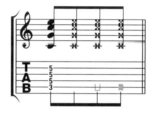

Repeated Chords
To make rhythm guitar parts easier to read the tablature numbers may be omitted when a chord is repeated. The example shows a C major chord played naturally, r/h muted, l/h muted and as an unpitched mute respectively.

Special Tunings
Non-standard tunings are shown as 'tuning boxes'. Each box represents one guitar string, the leftmost box corresponding to the lowest pitched string. The symbol '•' in a box means the pitch of the corresponding string is not altered. A note within a box means the string must be re-tuned as stated. For tablature readers, numbers appear in the boxes. The numbers represent the number of half-steps the string must be tuned up or down. The tablature relates to an instrument tuned as stated.

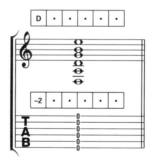

Tune the low E (6th) string down one tone (two half-steps) to D.

Chord naming
The following chord naming convention has been used:

Where there is no appropriate chord box, for example when the music consists of a repeated figure (or riff) the tonal base is indicated in parenthesis: [C]

Where it was not possible to transcribe a passage, the symbol ∼ appears.

Hinweise zu Notation und Tabulatur

Offener C - Dur - Akkord

E - Dur - Tonleiter

Hohe E-Saite (1.)
H-Saite (2.)
G-Saite (3.)
D-Saite (4.)
A-Saite (5.)
Tiefe E-Saite (6.)

Gezogene Noten

Die gegriffene Note wird immer zuerst angegeben. Das Zeichen ⌐ ¬ zeigt eine Veränderung der Tonhöhe an, die durch das Ziehen der Saiten erreicht wird. Falls Du nicht sicher bist, wie weit die Saite gezogen werden soll, spiele die entsprechenden Töne zunächst ohne Ziehen; so kannst Du Dich an der Tonhöhe orientieren. Die folgenden Beispiele geben die gebräuchlichsten Techniken zum Ziehen wieder:

Beispiel 1
Spiele das D und ziehe dann um einen Ton (zwei Halbtonschritte) höher zum E.

Beispiel 4
Im Voraus gezogen: Greife das D, ziehe um einen Ton höher zum E und schlage erst dann die Saite an.

Beispiel 2
Spiele das D, ziehe um einen Ton hoch zum E und dann wieder zurück, so daß D erklingt. Dabei wird nur die erste Note angeschlagen.

Beispiel 5
Spiele A und D gleichzeitig und ziehe dann die H-Saite um einen Ton nach oben, so daß H erklingt.

Beispiel 3
Schnelles Ziehen: Spiele das D und ziehe dann so schnell Du kannst um einen Ton höher zum E.

Beispiel 6
Spiele D und Fis gleichzeitig; ziehe dann die G-Saite um einen Ton nach oben zum E und die H-Saite um einen Halbtonschritt nach oben zum G.

Zusätzliche Spieltechniken für Gitarre wurden folgendermaßen notiert:

Tremolo
Verändere die Tonhöhe mit dem Tremolo-Hebel. Wenn es möglich ist, wird die angestrebte Tonhöhe angezeigt.
a) Spiele G; nutze den Takt, um zum E abzusteigen.
b) Spiele die leere G-Saite; nutze den Takt, um so weit wie möglich abzusteigen.

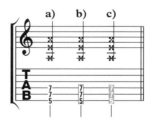

Dämpfen
a) Mit der rechten Hand
Dämpfe die Saiten, indem Du die rechte Hand einfach oberhalb der Brücke auf die Saiten legst.
b) Mit der linken Hand
Dämpfe die Saiten, indem Du den Druck der linken Hand löst, kurz nachdem die Töne erklingen.
c) Ohne bestimmte Tonhöhe
Dämpfe die Saiten mit der linken Hand; so erzielst Du einen 'geschlagenen' Sound.

Hammer on und Pull off
Spiele die erste Note; die zweite erklingt durch 'Hammering on', die dritte durch 'Pulling off'. Dabei wird nur die erste Note angeschlagen.

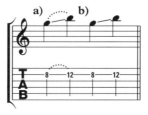

Glissando
a) Spiele die erste Note; die zweite erklingt durch Hochrutschen des Fingers auf der Saite. Nur die erste Note wird angeschlagen.
b) Wie oben, aber die zweite Note wird angeschlagen.

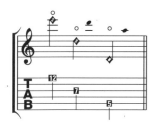

Natürliches Flageolett
Berühre die Saite über dem angegebenen Bund; wenn Du jetzt anschlägst, entsteht ein glockenähnlicher Ton. Wo es nötig ist, zeigen kleine Notenköpfe die entstandene Note an.

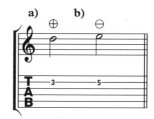

Slide Guitar
a) Spiele mit Rutschen des Fingers.
b) Spiele ohne Rutschen.

Künstliches Flageolett
Greife die unterste Note, berühre die Saite über dem durch Rauten angegebenen Bund und schlage dann den Ton an. Die kleinen Notenköpfe zeigen wieder die entstandene Note an.

Vibrato
Beim Vibrato läßt Du die Note für die Dauer eines Tons durch Druckvariation oder Tremolo-Hebel 'beben'. Da es jedoch eine Frage des persönlichen Geschmacks ist, wird Vibrato nur dort angegeben, wo es unerläßlich ist.

Gezupftes Flageolett
Greife die Note ganz normal, aber drücke die Saite mit der zupfenden Hand so, daß ein harmonischer Oberton entsteht. Kleine Notenköpfe zeigen den entstandenen Ton an.

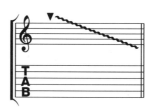

Pick Scratch
Fahre mit dem Plektrum nach unten über die Saiten – das klappt am besten bei umsponnenen Saiten.

Vierteltöne
Ein nach unten gerichteter Pfeil bedeutet, daß die notierte Tonhöhe um einen Viertelton erniedrigt wird; ein nach oben gerichteter Pfeil bedeutet, daß die notierte Tonhöhe um einen Viertelton erhöht wird.

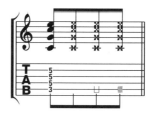

Akkordwiederholung
Um die Stimmen für Rhythmus-Gitarre leichter lesbar zu machen, werden die Tabulaturziffern weggelassen, wenn ein Akkord wiederholt werden soll. Unser Beispiel zeigt einen C - Dur - Akkord normal gespielt, rechts gedämpft, links gedämpft und ohne Tonhöhe.

Besondere Stimmung
Falls eine Stimmung verlangt wird, die vom Standard abweicht, wird sie in Kästchen angegeben. Jedes Kästchen steht für eine Saite, das erste links außen entspricht der tiefsten Saite. Wenn die Tonhöhe einer Saite nicht verändert werden soll, enthält das Kästchen einen Punkt. Steht eine Note im Kästchen, muß die Saite wie angegeben umgestimmt werden. In der Tabulaturschrift stehen stattdessen Ziffern im entsprechenden Kästchen: Sie geben die Zahl der Halbtonschritte an, um die eine Saite höher oder tiefer gestimmt werden soll.

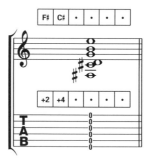

Stimme die tiefe E-Saite (6.) um einen Ganzton (zwei Halbtonschritte) höher auf Fis und die A-Saite (5.) um zwei Ganztöne (vier Halbtonschritte) höher auf Cis.

Akkordbezeichnung
Die folgenden Akkordbezeichnungen wurden verwendet.

Wenn kein eigenes Akkordsymbol angegeben ist, z.B. bei Wiederholung einer musikalischen Figur (bzw. Riff), steht die Harmoniebezeichnung in Klammern: [C]

Das Symbol ~ steht jeweils dort, wo es nicht möglich war, einen Abschnitt zu übertragen.

Printed by Halstan & Co.Ltd., Amersham, Bucks., England